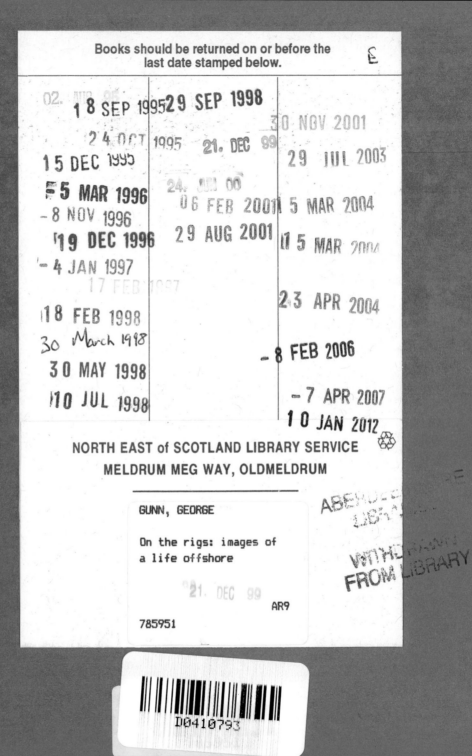

ON THE RIGS

Images of a
Life Offshore

Photographs by Allan Wright • Poems by George Gunn

Keepdate Publishing

Keepdate Publishing

Published by Keepdate Publishing Ltd,
21 Portland Terrace, Jesmond,
Newcastle upon Tyne NE2 1QQ.

FIRST EDITION 1995

ISBN 1 899506 00 4

AR9
785951

Designed and typeset by Keepdate Publishing Ltd, Newcastle upon Tyne.
Printed in Hong Kong.

Supported by

*This book is dedicated
to all those who know
the true price of oil.*

I grew up with the North Sea oil industry and it grew up with me. As it expanded and consolidated off the north Highland shores of Scotland in the early to late seventies I ended up working in it for those crucial seven years which take a lad from boyhood to manhood. The oil field is inside me. I am either a participant or a critic. These seem to be the only two valid positions to hold when you are talking oil. Ah, the macho politics of it all. There is no way around that, so there it is.

I and my generation were the residual working class males, easy to train, dependable and on hand. We were drafted in, aged eighteen, to the big industry. We were initiated into the ways of the oilman and we made their machines work. My brother and I, almost all of the boys in my village who did not go to university and some who did, ended up working on the rigs in the North Sea. Why? Was there a god in the soil or in the sea? Absolutely. It was called economics. In the seventies the Highlands was not a place to be young and unemployed. I remember watching with my brother, in sheer amazement, as Ted Heath confided to the nation on TV that Britain was in a state of full employment. It was a strange time. My brother went to university. I went and worked on the local paper. Before we realised it, we were both offshore; I wielding a scrubbing brush on the deck of a 'semi submersible' and he turning valves on a platform. From our north Highland home to there was a long journey. Short in distance perhaps, just a few hundred miles north or east, but long, if not epic, in consequence.

Many, many others like us came from the fields and farmyards of Buchan, from the fishing villages and the islands and the broad wet straths or valleys of the north. The first thing I ever saw offshore was a crane driver from Methil drown. He went over the side, his crane with him. Pulled down by the motion of the boat he was off loading. It was my first day on the rig. A month later the same thing happened. The crane driver this time came from Muir of Ord – but dead none the less. It was strange and hard to understand. We contributed to the riches and the success of the North Sea oil industry and it seemed to my young eyes then that we were paid a wage and expected to die. Dramatic perhaps, unreal, even, but the frenetic energy of the time ran through our blood like this. Another major thing happened. We met America. It was not the one we were used to. Not *The Man From Uncle* or Raymond Burr. They seemed to us to be insatiable and engaged upon some colonial slave mission. We were young, Celtic and Third World. Generally we got on fine.

During those years of the seventies it appeared as if there were given patterns, a set of inevitabilities, something that was ordained from above. Looking back, from the safety of now, I can see the stupidity of that. But at the time, acceptance was all.

The photographs in this book, along with the poems, represent a truth. 'A' truth as opposed to 'the' truth because truth is relative and if I have been politicised in any way by North Sea oil, it is because the oil industry represents capitalism gone mad. It's not as if drilling for oil in a shallow, turbulent ocean is a 'natural' process. When you are drilling for oil you are never one hundred percent sure that some force will not be unleashed and blow you out of the ocean. Against natural and unknown formation pressure you have to rely on mathematics and engineering: sometimes they offer poor protection.

Like most constructs of human endeavour the oil industry is rich in mythology. The prominent mythology is that things were always tougher and better in the oil field when the conveyor of this information was young. When the derricks were made of wood and the men were made of iron. Another myth is that everyone working offshore makes a fortune. Many oilmen do make a lot of money but for the majority – say for roughnecks[1] sweating over a pair of rig tongs[2] for two weeks every month – the take home pay is slightly above the national average. Most people have no conception about what life offshore is like. And how can they? Oil companies pay small fortunes to keep their public image very clean.

The life of the offshore oil worker may have its moments, but it is far from glamorous. For the average oil-hand arriving in Aberdeen the night before a crew change there is always a sense of foreboding. This is true no matter how many times you do it. But the mundane is always present. You are destined for an anonymous guest house, usually in Crown Street, to meet up with the other, non city dwelling members of your crew. There is nothing else to do but go out on the town. This is a group activity most oil hands are naturally good at. It is a kind of mutual bonding gone in for by warrior castes the world over since time began. And it is important. A roughneck, for example, is very much part of a crew. You live, work and sleep with the other crew members for half your life. You depend on them and they depend on you. Socialising soothes those raw nerve endings which will gel the various individuals into a working unit. The closer a rig crew feel together and the better they get on with one another the fewer accidents they will have offshore.

The following morning starts very early. Hungover heads encircle a breakfast table and a few stomachs turn and retreat from the cholesterol dripping fry-up placed unceremoniously before you by a cold-eyed Aberdonian landlady. Then it is off in the company bus to the heliport. The sensible mind switches off. The routine begins of checking in, waiting for your flight to be called, drinking coffee, the flight being called and then

---

1. Roughnecks: men who work on the drill floor of a drilling rig.
2. Rig Tongs: a set of giant spanners, much like pipe wrenches, with which the drill crew break out the drill string.

struggling into the survival suit (which, I was once reliably informed, was: "not ta keep ya dry, boy, but ta keep ya together if the chopper hits the ocean"). All this and the hangover-thumping noise of the chopper engine as it hurls you across the North Sea to the rig turns the brain to jelly by the time you stagger out onto the heli-deck. Now is the time to switch your brain back on, if you can. You go to your cabin which you may share with someone else from your crew, or you may not if you are lucky. You go up to the galley and have something to eat. You get ready for your 'tower' (shift). You start work. If you are a roughneck it is almost certain that they have 'pumped a slug' and are just about to pull out of the hole just as your chopper touched down. This means in English that they are about to pull the drill string out of the well in order to change the drill bit or some other part of the string. What it means in reality to a roughneck is six hours of uninterrupted toil. The first tower is only six hours long. After that it's twelve hours a day for the next fourteen. By the time midnight comes you have sore muscles and a beery, sweaty film beneath your coveralls, your eyelids are like lead canopies and your eyes are like two small red planets in the empty constellation of your head. But the shift is over, that's the important thing. You shower and try to eat something; no movie; too tired. You go to sleep. You've started your trip. Tomorrow won't be so bad – you hope.

The time goes. The days follow one another with bewildering speed. Each day is different and something new happens. I was involved in the drilling side of the industry. We were 'wildcaters', which means drilling exploration wells. It was, and still is, dangerous – working on the drill floor of a semi submersible drilling rig is one of the most dangerous occupations in the world. Not that we knew or cared about that. Drilling is a process. It is as controlled as it can be. There is little repetition unless there has been a 'fuck up!' No two weeks are the same, no two days are the same. From 'spud in' (commencement of drilling) to well test a variety of activities keeps the rig hand hard at it.

Men react differently. Some, quite wisely, run screaming after their first week to the heli-deck and weep. Others somehow tune into this sense of achieving something, of seeing the process working. Fortunately, or unfortunately, there is a sense too of thwarting nature, of succeeding despite all that she can throw at you. All this and more is a common mindset, running right through from toolpusher[3] to roustabout[4]. It is the collective consciousness of the roughneck and it kept me offshore for seven years. Despite my best efforts, it inhabits my head still. That oilscape is deep in my subconscious now. After all these years the dreams remain. Why should that be? The questions are easy. Perhaps it is because the oil field is a world of its own, with its own social structure and values. Perhaps it was the international mixture of the people I met, that my own kind, northern and innocent, could encounter nowhere else. There were Americans, of course. There were Glaswegians, Scousers, Geordies and men from every corner of the British Isles. There were Scandinavians, Poles, Dutch, Germans and French. Also New Zealanders, Australians, Canadians, South Africans, South Americans and Caribbeans. We travelled the whole world without leaving the North Sea. It was in many ways like a goldrush.

In the middle to late seventies there was a nervous excitement about the streets and pubs of Aberdeen which I imagine was similar to that of the Klondike or the Yukon. A tingling sense of expectancy gripped civic leaders and roughnecks alike. Scotland seemed to pulse. Oil terminals like Sullum Voe, Flotta and St Fergus were constructed in Shetland, Orkney and Buchan. Platform jacket construction yards were established at Kishorn in Wester Ross,

3. Toolpusher: Rig Superintendent in charge of drilling operations on the rig.
4. Roustabout: similar to a deckhand on a ship.

Nigg in Easter Ross, Ardesair in Moray and Methil in Fife. Pipelines were dug and lain the length and breadth of the little country of Scotland which had seen nothing like it since the days of the herring boom of the late nineteenth century. But this was serious money on a scale unknown before. It couldn't last and it didn't.

The middle and late eighties saw the price of oil plummet which caused a decrease in the production of crude oil and gas which meant a reduction in the number of exploratory wells drilled. But recessions come and go and the only ones who felt the cold draft of economic change were the rig crews who were paid off or hired on as the oil companies did or did not need them. The effect of this, coupled with the dichotic nature of life offshore – two on, two off/the rig, home – puts a great strain on male/female relationships. A lot of oilmen find an emotional life hard to sustain. A lot find it impossible. The true psychological cost of the oil field on the men who worked and work it can only be guessed at. I have seen grown men weeping their eyes out in the boot locker.

Contrary to the oil field myth, men are not made out of iron. If there is any romance in the business then it is in the nature of the sea and the earth's formations and all that that entails. One constituent part which is absent from current North Sea oil thinking is that of women. In the mid 1990s there are, on average, thirty thousand men working in the British sector of the North Sea. The amount of women offshore may be a couple of hundred. Men offshore become marginalised from the society of 'the beach', as oilmen refer to the outside world. They become alien from all those values most decent societies call 'common'. This might seem extreme. But the oil field is an extreme world. In an atmosphere of unnecessary 'hyper-machismo' the average male enters into a weird process of change. Especially if you're

Scottish. And even more if you're Highland. You realise at once that your value system is not the value system in operation. All that you once held sacred, gets dumped. The oil companies are quite matter of fact about this: If you can't hack it – jack it!

I had never seen pornography before I went offshore. But it was rife and very popular. When I first arrived on the rigs I was nineteen and struggling to make sense of the world. The two flames of sex and death flickered bright. But it was not sex; it was too graphic and not erotic. And it was not death; it was too cheap and there was no funeral. There seemed to be no consequence to either. My mind flooded like a Hydro Electric scheme. My mother was a midwife in an Atlantic parish and I was used to continuity and respect for the rhythm of birth, life and death. When I put on my hard hat for the first time, I left all that behind. I was exposed.

But you learn to deal with it. Once, when I was roughnecking, my relief came up to let me go some five minutes before he usually did. His name was Wullie and he came from Dundee. I thanked him, gladly, as we were tripping out of the hole[5] and the drilling mud was flying everywhere. I gaily made my way down to the changing shack and as I was crossing the pipe deck I saw the medic and a few roustabouts running up the stairs at the side of the V-door[6] to the drill floor. Instinctively I followed them. Wullie lay in a heap at the side of the rotary table. Everybody was shouting. A solid steel cover from the compensator block above the draw works, which pulls the pipe from the hole and up the derrick, had fallen on him. The left side of his body, from collar bone to hip, was broken. I stood with my mouth open, then took a hold of one end of the stretcher and carried him down to the medics. Two days later in an Aberdeen hospital he died from internal injuries. It should have been me. Years, like leaves off a tree, shook from me that day.

5. Tripping out of the hole: Term used when pulling the drill string out of the well in order to change the drill bit or some other part of the drill string.
6. V-Door: A long, V-shaped panel of metal that connects the drill floor with the pipe deck. Drill pipe, collars etc are lowered and hoisted via the V-door.

Life on a semi submersible drilling rig is a life of heavy metal. The world you inhabit heaves and swings on the ocean's surface. The North Sea can be a wild and beautiful place. Sometimes she stretches human engineering so far that it breaks and she laughs and swallows her prize. The sea is untamable. The formation of the earth's crust, like the sea, can be unpredictable. To interfere with the process of geology has a cost. It is the lives, such as Wullie's, lost.

I was young and strong, but I could see we were at the feet of oil money, naked capitalism. Oil shuts you down, hems you in, makes it hard to speak from inside. Oil companies, by their very nature, are like spoiled children; they will chance their arm, try to get away with anything, if you let them. They fall upon the resources, they exploit them and then they are constantly on the move – searching, ever searching. The economics of oil turn them into white sharks which can never rest. So the men go out upon the ocean and wrestle with the metal, they prod the earth and the big bucks come rolling in.

When I look back to those times of the seventies I see the youth of a nation almost as though it had gone to war. We suck the hydrocarbon deposits from the Orcadian basin of the North Sea and choppers go down and boats sink. Rigs break their anchors and drift. The *Ekofisk* has happened, the *Alexander Kielland* has happened. The *Piper Alpha* is a grim reality that could happen again.

Life on the rigs is not brilliant, it is hard, it is organised and I lived it. If there was any goodness in it, it is in the camaraderie of the men who do the work which allows the oil to flow. Wherever they come from, they are valuable men and the history of oil is always written in their blood.

The oil industry remains a hidden world. It is difficult to write its history. Most oil fields lie hundreds of miles offshore where they cannot be seen by the naked eye. They are physically mysterious. Oilmen tend not to talk about their world when they are ashore. Anyway, no one would understand them, not having the necessary reference points. The oil field, to most of the British public, is a modern Avalon. I remember driving to Fraserburgh with my aunt, a serious, intelligent and sober woman, and as she saw the early warning discs on the top of Mormond Hill, put there to warn of incoming Soviet missiles, she asked: "Is that the rigs?" This lack of awareness is common.

Further, the oil companies guard their public image with a zeal bordering on paranoia. They know the power of images. They strictly, rigorously control their public images – what the public are allowed to see. So the mystery remains.

Television, theatre, and the media in general, help contribute to the mystery of life offshore. A recent British television series on the oil industry portrayed life on the rigs as something between *Brookside* and 'James Bond'. It is not so.

Oil is one of Britain's primary industries which has made a huge contribution to government spending. Perhaps that, more than anything, is why the culture and the reality of the North Sea oil industry has been kept a deliberate mystery. This book opens some doors on the industry.

Some time ago, the formula of oil worker input and oil company protection broke down. One hundred and sixty seven men, just like me, were killed when the *Piper Alpha* exploded into one, then two, fireballs. 'Murder' may be too strong a word. After that apocalyptic night in 1988 the face of the oil field changed. Whatever you call it, the 'Worker/Company deal', as Burns would say, 'went a gley'. Trust and innocence were shaken. The true cost of the oil finally hit home to a nation that, unbeknown to itself, depended on it. Something hard 'latched', like a set of drill pipe elevators, on to British society. In Scotland it was as if we had gone back to the Battle of the Somme. To the oil companies it was a hardening of the arteries. The oil worker now lives in a climate where British unions, if they are not banned, are certainly not encouraged.

Today, if an oil hand publicly, or on the rig, criticises an oil company he may not be sacked, or run off, but he is likely to get an NRB (Not Required Back) letter in the post. There have been strikes since the *Piper Alpha* disaster. As a result, there are now blacklists in operation where workers are effectively denied a job offshore. I remember in the early eighties, when I was an assistant driller, we held safety meetings every week, where the rig crew talked over and through every aspect of the drilling operation (whatever it was), and the suitability and safety of those procedures and the equipment we worked with. There were, by the very nature of things, criticisms. After all, we were trying to do a good job and, at the same time, stay alive. In the current climate in operation offshore we would all likely be NRB'd for our trouble. Nowadays, "Whatever you say, say nothing" is the sticker seen on most roughnecks' hardhats.

The breakdown in worker/company relationship will not do the oil companies any good in the long run, just as much as it does no good for the oil hand in the short term. Safety, instead of being the common coinage of the rig crews as it was before the slack years set in, is now a kind of branding iron. Safety, as I knew it, was not a word, it was a state of mind. I worked in one of the most dangerous environments there is for seven years and I still have all my fingers. That is a roughnecking success story.

But life offshore is not all gloom and doom. The Offshore Industry Liaison Committee (OILC) could become the one big union in the oil industry which both workers and companies really need. It is to their mutual benefit. The OILC is the type of organisation that can heal the fear and paranoia, the insecurity and shortsightedness, that is crippling one of Britain's most important major industries.

I grew up with the oil industry and it grew up with me. Both of us now are approaching middle age and perhaps both are entering that crisis period. All I can say in relation to the North Sea oil field is that I fear for those young ones who go into her now. I fear for their chances and I fear for their safety. This is a book about an industry which changes rapidly, but at a fundamental level stays the same. Equipment modernises and automation increases, men grow old and retire or die, but the process of drilling for oil, and the desire to do it, remains constant.

But the North Sea fields are approaching the end of their lives and the new fields are smaller. How long it will last I do not know. Twenty, thirty years? Predictions are dangerous. But in the end, for me, the oil industry does not matter. What matters is the people who work that industry. The mud spattered roughneck; the crane driver in his cab; the toolpusher in his office; the roustabout in the smoke-shack. They are real and they are yet but dreams flitting across my mind like a hayfield that tickles my nostrils in the early summer with its wet sweetness. This book is theirs. Every ugly, beautiful one of them. I miss them, but I am not fooled into thinking they miss me.

George Gunn

ON THE RIGS

For seven years I cut my lip
on your temporary needles
one roughneck with spliced
northern music, my Norwegian hand

my Scottish hand, can you see them
between semi sub and production
jacket, they are holding onto rig-tong
and coastline, my hands are singing

roustabout, derrickman, they are clapping
the mud and the gas, they are feeling
the footings and the casings of history
our small story, my hands are their verbs

It is time now to see the clear sea water
and the price of our lives

North Sea storm. The safety boat battles heavy seas to stay on location.

CREW CHANGE

Up, out and over, dark heavy laid seas
Shetland, scattered left, long and sparse
The chopper hurtles us out to the Sinbad
Beneath, on white foaming legs, a boat

                    crouches through waves
                        shambolic yet intent

I gaze East; vague the horizon wilts
Under lead grey cloud, light spears
Through like Winter's heavenly wound
Like a purpose through man's doubt

                    a low cut North Sea
                        of drilling & moving

This is the oil industry & rocked
By waved elements it is giving birth
This child is hungry still, this
Young one was born hard & ugly

                    its mouth always
                        gluttonous to the last

I slouch back in my seat & escape
Predestination, I am unconscious of fatherhood
I am one in a family of waste, wanting
Nothing more than heli-deck, cabin berth

                    ignoring waste, thinking maybe
                        it will never save anything

Crew change, inward flight.

A rude delivery from the warm cabin of the chopper on to the heli-deck in a Force 5. Hot kerosene exhaust from the Sea King's engines strikes the faces of the crew.

Dawn through the V-door.

THE SEA'S KISS

We wait lightly for the sea's kiss
Together, then alone, our shore line
Hugs closely around vain communions
The bay of our expectant arrivals

waiting, through smoke
over platform & barge

Foreign accents again lead easily
Roustabout, roughneck, we labour
Unknowingly & we learn well
Crane driving, chain spinning

drill floors egg hunger
pipe decks store fate

I have worked derricks for three years now
The future is only a past, waiting
Cobwebs hang from compensator block
Rust chews eventually into drill pipe, collar, tong

I have here for you
no remedies

RIG FLOOR

Make that tong bite, and go home
to the boat & the village
pull those slips and return
to the steading & the byre

Tripping pipe through a small eternity
hard hats & gloves, redwings
& dickies, the mudded uniform
of the tired & burnt roughneck

The pipe-spinner will not twist your head
around to the future or count
your fingers & your years
as you go back, back to the place

that gave you breath & lung
locked as you are in a small
battle dying singularly
in a larger war, how much longer

will you stare at the drill bit
of a one way journey
better to latch the elevators
around the tooljoint of your own dreams

Drill pipe and a glimpse of roughnecks 'running pipe' on the drill floor.

A new drill bit, just fitted to the drill string. It is carefully guided through the rotary table at the start of its trip to the bottom of the hole, perhaps 10,000 feet below. A bit may last 10 to 40 hours, depending on the rock formation it has to cut through.

'Wet trip': roughnecks working the breakout tongs. A 'wet trip' occurs when the mud in the hole is out of balance with the mud in the drill pipe. The situation is aggravated here by the cloying, smelly oil-based drilling mud in use.

Roughneck crew latching the casing elevators.

A roughneck is hoisted up into the derrick wearing a riding belt attached to a hydraulic tugger. His mission: to free a tangled cable.

THE DERRICKMAN

Bird of the monkey board
pulling out of the hole
eyes like chipped marbles
wrapped up in a hanky

never eat, stomach tight against belt
tied to the derrick like a bouy
to pull stand after stand
until the hair on the head swims

and breakfast flies through the air
like an exploded grouse
and the only glory a raxed back
and the elastic arms of a sad gorilla

a human machine part
of blood and rope
a sentry of muscles
on the way to the sky

and through the gate of the seabed
we are digging, digging
into the formation where the thing
that will finally hold us is waiting

Derrickman in action on the monkey board. He is 100 feet above the drill floor and precariously racking stands of drill pipe whilst the operation 'pulls out of' or 'runs into' the hole.

Tooljoints.

TOOLJOINTS

Scarred by tong-dies, stacked at the end
of a stand, rattling out their tensile music
as the rig heaves on the swell
the tooljoints join and separate one world

from the next, boxes for threads
pins for penetration in industrial
coupling but no love amongst
these connections, only zinc-dope and bushings

a racked tribe of utilitarians, a currency
of drilling mud & muscle
my shoulder hugged you
to throw you in or pull you out

long years we sucked at the heart
of the world, man & metal
a failed marriage on a submersible
set of images turning green

The sea won't remember us, the holes
we drill will be plugged up
The drill-pipe stands racked in the derrick
like matches waiting to be struck

Rig dawn.

Foggy dawn.

Technicians install gauges on drill string for well test while a petroleum engineer records data.

Breakfast fuel up. Four full meals are cooked every 24 hours and there are no restrictions on consumption.

Deck scrubber. A career on the rig often starts here.

Derrickman fits a new tensioner line to the marine riser, which acts like a giant suspension unit and allows the semi submersible rig to ride the waves yet constantly keeping it in touch with the well. Safety lines are a must in the 'moon pool area'.

Serious discussion in the driller's console.

The pipe deck. The barge engineer, O.I.M. (Offshore Installation Manager), toolpusher, crane driver, petroleum engineer, cementer and a roughneck discuss the jobs in hand.

GREASY SPAR

Amid this world, evening sits grey on the hill
Sad, by the extinct volcano, you sit
Where the North winds resound, amid waves
I have dry tides in my throat

I hear clanging metal, motioning structures, reverberations
Across this rich sea, piped ashore, refined
Sweat drips, blood, black steel
Orange flare offs on the horizon

Womb furnaces, melody of lips, swing booms
Hung over used sea space, drilled locations
Geology's fruit; sad, by this tapped fountain
You sit, on the hill of winds

Who but you could hear these sea beat agonies
I hang un-voiced from a greasy spar
Shoreless, my silence around, let me hear
Your voice, amid these stormy tragedies

A roustabout paints the crane jib support.

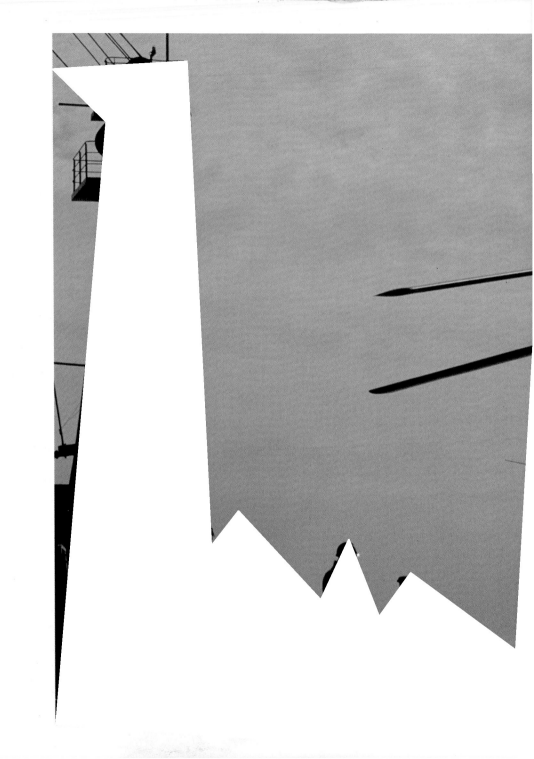

The crew attends a
Sea King chopper.

Harry 'the Steel'; a roughneck in the derrick helping out with the casing run.

SLIPS
(for Bob Saville)

We will set our swords down
our rig tongs and our shields
and we will walk away from battle
from drill floor and from time
I will remember you there
roughneck of the longboat
the crew change and the video raid
I have found you here
beside the drill bit
and the spear point
where none before me could
say: my brother was
in your crew and he kept
all his fingers, from the Brent
to the Volga, we pump and we row

A retired North Sea trawler as stand by/ safety boat in heavy seas. Rig men watching these small boats in such weather admire the hardiness of the crews.

HUNG OFF

Four degree pitch, roll & heave, running
In the hole, drill bit hungry
Rig floor movement, bruising
Independent hung tongs etc, swinging

Roughnecks jump & dodge ape shit
Drill pipe, unwanting smacks from tooljoints
Driller worried slightly, toolpusher
Anxious always, the weather wins

We have only so much power, method
Elastic to a point (the derrickman rubs
His bruised fingers) can only stretch
But not to extremes, and these are extremities

We cancel progress & process for some hours
Waiting-on-weather written down
On drilling report, idle pleasure
For floorhands; impressively the wind

Has dull blasted the light from the remaining day
Over on the horizon platforms buffet and cower
The sky, wet with impendence, closes
In: one rig, weather hit, hung off

Smokoe shack. A converted container on deck acts as a coffee shop for workers to rest and take a hot drink and a smoke.

W.O.W (Waiting On Weather). On the drill floor a service hand reads a five-day old copy of The Sun. Bad weather, which can last for several days, causes normal activities to be suspended for safety reasons.

A crane cab. Great skill is required in order to lift and drop heavy loads on and off boat decks that are moving with the swell. It is dangerous work and it is not unknown for crane and driver to be pulled off the rig (see text).

Deck hands catching some sun on the attendant supply boat before off loading the 9⅝ casing.

Crane operator at work.
Intense concentration
is required.

Technician sets instrument on downhole tool while roughnecks look on. During drilling this system will provide data on downhole conditions which are relayed to the surface for analysis.

BROKEN TOW LINES

With grief we will expire
We will not stay, my lady
We of easy gain, empty
In the privilege of life

                    we, pale in the Winter-House
                      have not used up eternity

We of petty wealth, we of dollars
Spent in Aberdeen hotels, we of £10 tips
Making hole in the soft caress of possibility
Crew changing out of one sadness to the next

              we, like the moon on the Western wave
                        rest hardly

We of $32 a minute, hire this rig, deep well
We of tobacco spit, we of fast trip time
We of trying to get on, we of trying to live
Lady, we are building heli-decks on a country

                      ravaged so gently
                    we of broken tow lines

Dusk on the rig.

Hard hat erotica. A close look
reveals one man's fantasy.

'Tomb of the Unknown Roughneck'. The
barrel acts as an anchor during 'spud in'.

'Butch'. Scottish rig superintendent who started his working life on the trawlers.

Water cannon and
well test flare.

A mud soaked roughneck descends
from the drill floor at the end of his 'tour'.

SCRUBBING BRUSH

Down by the moonpool they were changing their minds
Dickie cover-alls and Macdonald-T's
roughnecks gloves hanging over their hips
watching the mud riser going up and down
and one of them said 'How do they do that?'
and I gripped my scrubbing brush so tight
it became a schiltren of Robert the Bruce
and then an Aberdonian voice said 'It's no
the riser that's goin' up an doon, it's the fucking rig!'
and he went back to his welding job
They took the American away and fed him T-bone steak and prawns
and he sat there like a fat monkey
We longed each week for the gloves they never used
I threw my scrubbing brush over the side

Petroleum engineers admiring their handiwork as a well is tested. Amidst great heat, artificial precipitation and numbing vibration, enough fuel is spent in one day to drive a small car twenty million miles. If the well is not deemed economic, global warming is all that is achieved.

A rig superintendent takes a
break while the Statfjord C inches
its way across the horizon.

ALEXANDER KIELLAND

(The Alexander Kielland, a semi-submersible drilling rig, whilst acting as a floating hotel to the Edda platform on 26th March 1980, turned turtle & within 6 minutes 120 men were lost.)

The rec room suddenly full of water, dark horizons
Slant, projector light flickers then images fade
Lungs now full of ocean air, thick and deathly
120 transfers from the live show

> to the dead show
> no encore, no reel change

Hope, like a flickering match, is consumed
The quickest 6 minutes all lives were to know
Struggling helpless in a design failure
A bumper harvest for the greedy sea morgue

> & what time does it close
> it never closes

Bodies stamped with full payment, yet
To be collected from the bank of their end
120 deposits in this unfilled wet vault
Who tells of such countings, who reasons, who reasons

> choppers search eagerly
> for lost change

Mystery shrouds the principal of being
Wave crest over hands desperately clutching
At a fate sealed by oblivion, a cargo
Of wreckage & despair turned turtle

> in the storm hungry
> Spring evening

Then, as morning ghosted in, lifejackets abandoned
Rafts, barrels floating, face down
Hidden in the gullies of wave after wave
Those who had no time left, whose eyes

> left behind work
> left memories

The underside of a semi-submersible in a heavy sea. The white pipe in the centre is the marine riser which connects the well to the surface drilling equipment.

Rescue zone.
(See Piper poem.)

The Norwegian engineer takes a break
while the rig moves through the sea.

A rare sunny day on the rig. Hot days offered an opportunity to create the illusion that you were somewhere else. This off watch leisure activity was recently banned.

Ball bearings.

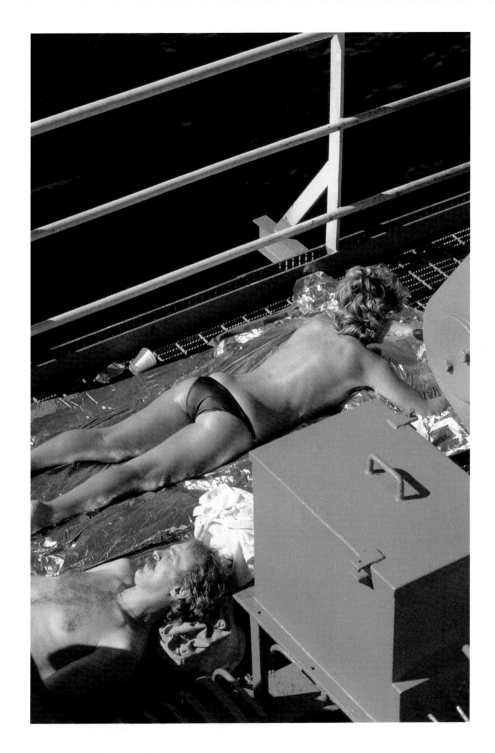

The rig medic in the sun.

Blue shots for red eyes. Some crew members slipped into the habit of watching the same porno flicks over and over again until their eyes and minds glazed over.

Service hand on his 'scratcher'.

Cementing engineer heaves a heavy hose through ankle deep water.

The Sikorsky S61
Sea King.

The 'night pusher' having fun with 'equipment familiarisation'. These powerful water canons are routinely used to keep the rig superstructure cool during high intensity (flare-off) well tests.

Radio operator. In repose, but there would usually be plenty of 'secretarial work' to keep him busy.

Dolphin man and his shiny hard hat. Such hard hats are now banned for safety reasons. In their heyday they offered some individuality to the rig hand prepared to do the polishing.

Rig medic filleting red mullet. The fishing was particularly good at this location and she accumulated a large quantity for the freezer during her two weeks hitch.

Moon light on the drill floor. In the background is casing being hoisted through the V-door ready to be lowered into the open hole.

Rig sky.

Rig sea.

North Sea: a rare calm day. Taking advantage of the fine weather the crane operator places a couple of roustabouts in a bucket, suspends them over the side and, until lunchtime, lets them paint the rig.

Rig Move: down near the pontoons upon which the rig floats. The rig heads to a new location 55 miles to the south. Semi-submersibles generally have their own means of propulsion but, for safety, they are always towed by a powerful supply/tug vessel. Its lights are just visible.

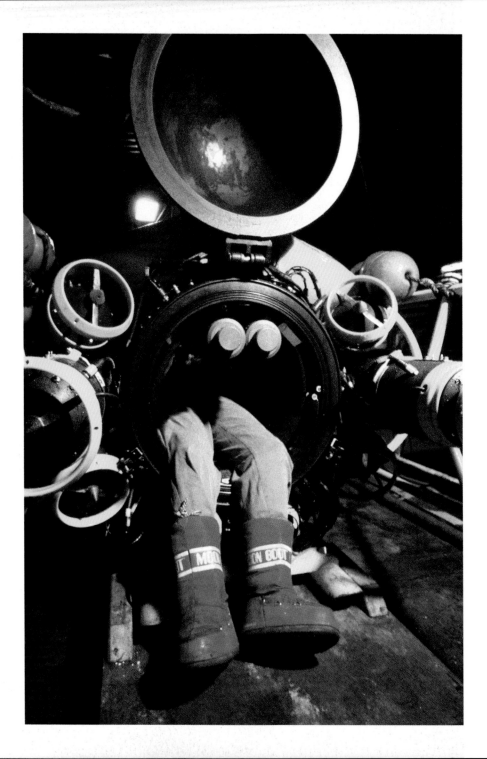

Trouble shooting deep sea diving teams rely upon high-tech mini-subs for sub sea maintenance operations.

'Midnight
nautilus'.

Somewhere on every rig deck there is a smokoe shack such as this for the sole purpose of grabbing a bite, smoking, drinking tea or coffee and 'shooting the bull'.

The pipe deck.

Well test.

Tongs repair.

The Sea King takes centre stage. Landing on the heli-deck with the safety boat in attendance.

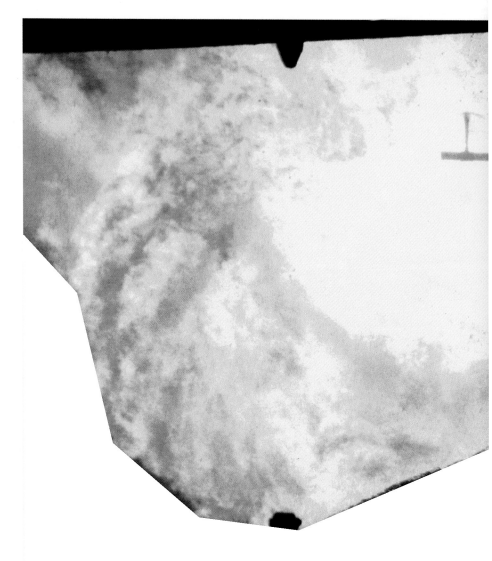

The well test. The climax of a successful wildcat drilling operation is the well test. A petroleum engineer toasts his ear while observing an 8,000 barrels a day flare off. Heavy vibration and pressure-fed humidity accompany the flare off.

Coming into Aberdeen. The other way of moving oil. An Esso tanker approaches its berth.

Calm before a serious storm.

Roughneck hanging
from tugger line.

Supply vessel as tug,
assisting a rig move.

Back loading casing
from supply boat.

PIPER

(For the 167 dead of the Piper 'Alpha')

My eyes are rivers of fire
and the dead feed on my chorus
on the smoke of a billowing column
on the applause of the bacon smellers
glad that they have not become
the plastic waft of melted hard hats
drifting over the gentle Summer sea
filled now with the black blood
of engineering and the fragile idolatry
of an unthought taking
    I see human tissue
turn to gas screaming its tune
of dolorous thanks through the twisted
rig legs and derrick girders flickered like pins
at the two handed dumbshow of finance and metal
and the dead sink in the neutral water
so many dead it is hardly bearable
they are at home now in the place of their origin
they fill my voice with their angry song
they sing
    "Up you, mate
    Up you" from under the feature pages
of middle brow papers
list after list like nineteen fourteen
roughneck and roustabout, crane-op and cook
name after name in numbing insistence
singing
    "Back in Buchan the barley is turning

in Scotland now the Summer is green"
    My eyes see the hush-up shape and begin
from within Texan lawyers' attache cases
it flies out, like a soul, at press conferences
like an invisible smog it both disappears and is seen
paving the way for back-handed payoffs
taking a loan of misery and grief
losing the place while we all watched
grown men confidently hoping that Red Adair
in his red asbestos longjohns
would ride out from the sunset
rewind the movie and make it ok
    This then the dream world of industrial oil
night after night it gets worse
the hush-up has swollen
to the size of Tehran
they park their Cadillacs in sinister places
and watch the sky burn like a torch
between the broken arms of the flare-off booms
holding the horizon still
for the many camera crews
so that we can all ooh and ahh
feeling pity in our armchairs at the TV news
    I, a roughneck, tell you this
from the strange country of disbelief
the dead are always with us
we remember the dead